junie b. jones®
and the
Stupid Smelly Bus

by BARBARA PARK

illustrated by

Denise Brunkus

To Cody—
who missed his bus
and inspired this book

Junie B. Jones and the Stupid Smelly Bus by Barbara Park

Text copyright © 1992 by Barbara Park
Cover art and interior illustrations copyright © 1992 by Denise Brunkus
All rights reserved.

This bilingual edition was published by Longtail Books in 2021 by arrangement with Barbara Park c/o Writers House LLC through KCC(Korea Copyright Center Inc.), Seoul.

ISBN 979-11-91343-08-3 14740

Longtail Books

Contents

1
Meeting Mrs.

My name is Junie B. Jones. The B **stand**s **for** Beatrice. **Except** I don't like Beatrice. I just like B and **that's all**.

I'm almost six years old.

Almost six is when you get to go to **kindergarten**. Kindergarten is where you go to meet new friends and not watch TV.

My kindergarten is the afternoon kind.

Today was my first day of school. I'd

been to my room before, though. Last week Mother took me there to meet my teacher.

It was called Meet the Teacher Day. My teacher was **decorating** the **bulletin board** with the letters of the alphabet.

"I already know all of those letters," I said. "I can sing them. Except I don't feel like it right now."

My teacher shook my hand. Only our hands didn't **fit** together that good.

Her name was Mrs.—I can't remember the rest of it. Mrs. said I looked cute.

"I know it," I said. "That's because I have on my new shoes."

I held my foot way high in the air.

"See how **shiny** they are? Before I put them on, I **lick**ed them.

Lucille
Junie
William

"And guess what else?" I said. "This is my bestest[1] hat. Grampa[2] Miller bought it for me. See the **devil horns stick**ing out the sides?"

Mrs. laughed. Except I don't know why. Devil horns **are supposed to** be **scary**.

Then we walked around the room and she showed me where **stuff** was. Like the easels[3] where we get to paint. And the **shelves** where the books are. And the tables where we sit and don't watch TV.

One of the tables in the front of the room had a red chair. "I would like to sit

---

1 **bestest** 단어 'best(최고의)'를 강조한 비격식적인 표현. '최고로 좋은' 이라는 뜻을 나타내며 어린아이가 주로 사용한다.

2 **grampa** '할아버지(grandpa)'를 부르는 말로, 'gramp', 'grampa', 'grampy' 등 다양한 표현이 있다.

3 **easel** 이젤. 그림을 그릴 때 캔버스나 화판을 놓는, 높낮이와 각도를 조절할 수 있는 받침대.

here, I think," I told her.

But Mrs. said, "We'll have to wait and see, Junie."

"B!" I said. "Call me Junie *B*.!"

I **holler**ed the B part real loud. So she wouldn't forget it.

People are *always* forgetting my B.

Mother **roll**ed **her eyes** and looked at the **ceiling**. I looked up there, too. But I didn't see anything.

"Are you going to **ride** the bus, Junie B.?" Mrs. asked me.

I made my shoulders go up and down. "I don't know. Where's it goin' to?"

My mother **nod**ded her head and said, "Yes, she'll be riding the bus."

That made me feel scary inside. 'Cause I

never rided[4] on a bus before.

"Yeah, only where's it goin' to?" I asked again.

Mrs. sat on her desk. Then she and my mother talked more about the bus.

I **tap**ped on Mrs.

"Guess what? I still don't know where it's goin' to."

Mrs. smiled and said the bus driver's name was Mr. Woo.

"Mr. Woo," said Mother. "That's an easy name for Junie B. to remember."

I **cover**ed my ears and **stamp**ed my foot. "YEAH, ONLY WHERE'S THE

---

4 **rided** (rode) 영어권 국가의 아이들이 동사의 과거형을 말할 때 모든 단어의 끝에 '-ed'를 붙이는 실수를 종종 한다. 이 책에 나오는 'bended (bent)', 'hanged(hung)' 등이 이와 같은 경우이다.

STUPID **SMELLY** BUS GOIN' TO?"

Mother and Mrs. **frown**ed.

Frowning is when your **eyebrow**s look **grumpy**.

"**Watch yourself**, missy,[5]" said Mother.

Missy's my name when I'm in trouble.

I looked down at my shoes. They didn't look as shiny as they did before.

Just then another mother and a boy came in. And Mrs. went off to talk to them **instead** of me. I don't know why, though. The boy was hiding behind his mother and acting very **babyish**. I can **beat** that boy up, I think.

After that, my mother sat me down and explained about the bus. She said it's yellow. And it's called a school bus. And it

---

5 **missy** '아가씨'라는 뜻으로 화나 애정을 담아 어린 여성을 부르는 표현.

stops at the end of my street.

Then I get on it. And sit down. And it takes me to school.

"And then your teacher will meet you in the **parking lot**," said Mother. "Okay, Junie B.? Won't that be fun?"

I nodded the word *yes*.

But inside my head I said the word *no*.

2
Feeling Squeezy[1]

I stayed **scare**d about the bus for a whole week. And last night when my mother **tuck**ed me into bed, I still felt **sickish** about it.

"Guess what?" I said. "I don't think I want to **ride** that school bus to **kindergarten**

---

1 **squeezy** 주니 B.가 만들어 낸 단어로 동사 'squeeze(꼭 쥐다)'의 뒤에 '-y'를 붙여 '쥐어짜는'이라는 의미의 형용사로 사용하였다. 이 책에 나오는 'whishy', 'peeky' 등이 이와 같은 경우이다.

tomorrow."

Then my mother **rumple**d my hair. "Oh, sure you do," she said.

"Oh, sure I don't," I said back.

Then Mother kissed me and said, "It'll be fun. You'll see. Just don't worry."

I did, though. I worried very much. And I didn't sleep so good, either.

And this morning I felt very **droopy** when I got up. And my **stomach** was squeezy. And I couldn't eat my cereal.

And so I watched TV until Mother said it was time to get ready to go.

Then I put on my skirt that looks like velvet.[2] And my new **fuzzy** pink sweater.

---

2 **velvet** 벨벳. 짧고 부드러운 솜털이 있고 광택이 나는 고급 원단.

And I ate half a **tuna** sandwich for lunch.

After that, Mother and I walked to the corner to wait for the bus.

And guess what? There was another mother and little girl there, too. The little girl had **curly** black hair—which is my favorite kind of head.

I didn't say hello to her, though. 'Cause she was from a different street, that's why.

Then finally this big yellow bus came around the corner. And the **brake**s

screeched very loud. And I had to **cover**

my ears.

Then the door opened.

And the bus driver said, "Hi! I'm Mr.

Woo. **Hop** on!"

Except I didn't hop on. 'Cause my legs

didn't want to.

"I don't think I want to ride this bus to

kindergarten," I told Mother again.

Then she gave me a little push. "**Go on**,

Junie B.," she said. "Mr. Woo is waiting

for you. Be a big girl and get on."

I looked up at the windows. The little girl with the curly black hair was already in the bus. She looked very big sitting up there. And kind of happy.

"Look how big *that* little girl is acting, Junie B.," said Mother. "Why don't you sit right next to her? It'll be fun. I promise."

And so I got on the bus.

And guess what?

It wasn't fun.

3
The Stupid Smelly Bus

The bus wasn't like my daddy's car at all. It was very big inside. And the seats didn't have any **cloth** on them.

The little **curly** girl was sitting near the front. And so I **tap**ped on her.

"Guess what?" I said. "Mother said for me to sit here."

"No!" she said. "I'm saving this seat for my best friend, Mary Ruth Marble!"

Then she put her little white **purse** on the place where I was going to sit.

And so I **made a face** at her.

"Hurry up and find a seat, young lady," said Mr. Woo.

And so I quick sat down across from the curly **mean** girl. And Mr. Woo shut the door.

It wasn't a **regular** kind of door, though. It **fold**ed in half. And when it closed, it made a **whish**y sound.

I don't like that kind of door. If it closes on you by **accident**, it will cut you in half, and you will make a **squishy** sound.

The bus made a big **roar**. Then a big **puff** of black smelly **smoke** came out the back end of it. It's called bus breath, I think.

Mr. Woo drove for a while. Then the **brake**s made that loud, **screechy** noise again. I **cover**ed my ears so it couldn't get inside my head. 'Cause if loud, screechy noises get inside your head, you have to take an aspirin.[1] I saw that on a TV **commercial**.

Then the bus door opened again. And a dad and a boy with a **grouchy** face got on.

The dad smiled. Then he **plop**ped the grouchy boy right next to me.

"This is Jim," he said. "I'm afraid Jim isn't too happy this afternoon."

The dad kissed the boy good-bye. But

---

1 **aspirin** 아스피린. 해열, 진통, 항염에 작용하는 가정상비약.

the boy **wipe**d it off his **cheek**.

Jim had on a **backpack**. It was blue.

I love backpacks. I wish I had one of my very own. One time I found a red one in a **trash** can. But it had a little bit of **gushy** on it, and Mother said no.

Jim's backpack had lots of **zipper**s. I touched each one of them.

"One . . . two . . . three . . . four," I **count**ed.

Then I un**zip**ped one.

"HEY! DON'T!" **yell**ed Jim.

He zipped it right up again. Then he moved to the seat in front of me.

I hate that Jim.

After that, the bus kept stopping and starting. And lots of kids kept getting on.

Loud kids. And some of them were the kind who look like **meanie**s.

Then the bus began getting very noisy and hot inside. And the sun kept shining down on me and my **fuzzy** hot sweater.

And here's another hot thing. I couldn't **roll** down my window because it didn't have a **handle**. And so I just kept on getting hotter and hotter.

And it smelled in the bus, too. The bus smelled like an egg salad sandwich.

"I want to get off of here," I said right out loud. But nobody heard me. "I hate it in this stupid smelly bus."

Then my eyes got a little bit wet. I wasn't crying, though. 'Cause I'm not a baby, that's why.

After that, my nose started running. Only the bus didn't have a **glove compartment**. Which is where you keep the travel **tissue**s, of course. And so I had to wipe my nose on my fuzzy pink sweater **sleeve**.

Then I stayed on the bus for about an hour or three. Until finally I saw a **flagpole** and a **playground**.

That meant we were at kindergarten!

Then Mr. Woo drove the bus into the **parking lot** and stopped.

I jumped up very fast. 'Cause all I wanted to do was get off that stupid smelly thing!

Only guess what? That Jim pushed right in front of me. And the curly mean

girl did, too. And then people started **squish**ing me real tight. And so I pushed them away. And they pushed me right back.

That's when I fell down! And a big foot stepped on my skirt that looks like velvet.

"STOP IT!" I yelled.

Then Mr. Woo **holler**ed, "HEY, HEY, HEY!"

And he picked me up. And helped me off the bus.

Mrs. was waiting for me just like my mother said.

"Hi! I'm glad to see you!" she called.

Then I ran over to her. And I showed her the big **footprint** on my skirt that looks like velvet.

"Yeah, only look what happened. I got stepped on and so now I'm **soil**ed."

Mrs. **brush**ed it. "Don't worry, Junie," she said. "It'll **come off**."

After that I just folded my arms and made a **frown**.

'Cause guess what?

She forgot my B again.

4
Me and Lucille
and Some Other Kids

Some of the other bus kids **turn**ed **out** to be in my class, too.

One of them was that Jim.

That Jim I hate.

Mrs. made us **line up**. Then we followed her to our room. Its name is Room Nine.

There were other kids waiting by the door. When Mrs. un**lock**ed it, everyone

squeezed in all **at once**.

That Jim stepped on my new shoe. He made a **scratch mark** on my **shiny toe**. The kind of scratch that **lick**ing won't fix.

"HEY! WATCH IT, YOU **DUMB** JIM!" I hollered at him.

Mrs. **bent** down next to me. "Let's try to use our quiet voice while we're in school," she said.

I **nod**ded nicely. "I hate that Jim," I said in my quiet voice.

After that, Mrs. **clap**ped her hands together very loud.

"I want everyone to find a chair and sit down as fast as you can," she said.

That's when I ran to the table with the red chair. Only guess what? There was already someone sitting there! A girl with little red **fingernail**s.

And so I tapped on her and said, "I would like to sit there, I think."

"No," she said. "*I* am."

"Yeah, only I already picked that chair out," I told her. "Ask my mother if you don't believe me."

But the girl just shook her head no.

And then Mrs. clapped her loud hands again and said, "Please find a seat!"

And so then I had to quick sit down in a stupid yellow chair.

The same stupid color as the stupid yellow bus.

After that, Mrs. walked to a big **closet** in the back of the room. It's called the **supply** closet. She got out boxes of new **pointy** crayons[1] and some white circles. Then she passed them out. And we had to **print** our names on the circles and **pin** them to our fronts.

It was our first work.

"If you need help **spell**ing your name, raise your hand," said Mrs.

I raised my hand.

"I don't need help," I told her. "Grandma Miller says I print beautifully."

I used red. But then a mistake happened. I made my **JUNIE** too big and there wasn't any **room** left for my **B.** And so I had to **squish** it very **teeny** at the

---

1 **crayon** 크레용. 그림을 그릴 때 사용하는 연필 모양의 채색 도구. 안료 에 파라핀 등을 섞은 후 녹여서 만든다.

bottom.

"I HATE THIS STUPID DUMB CIRCLE!" I hollered.

Mrs. made the *shhh* sound and gave me a new one.

"Thank you," I said nicely. "Grandma Miller says I print beautifully."

The girl with the little red fingernails

was faster than me. She showed me her

circle and pointed to her letters.

"L-U-C-I-L-L-E. That spells *Lucille*," she

said.

"I like that name of Lucille," I said.

"'Cause guess why? Seals[2] are my favorite

---

2 **seal** 바다표범. 물범과의 포유류로 몸의 길이는 1.5~2미터이며, 잿빛 바탕에 작고 검은 점이 있다. 여기에서 주니 B.는 루실(Lucille)의 이름과 비슷한 발음 때문에 이 동물을 떠올렸다.

animals. That's why."

Then Mrs. passed out drawing paper. And we drew pictures of our family.

Mrs. put a happy-face sticker on mine.

It was very good. **Except** I made my father too teeny. And Mother's hair looked like **stick**s.

After that, Mrs. took our class on a walk around the school. Everyone had to find a **buddy** to walk with.

My buddy was Lucille. We held hands.

The boy I can **beat** up was right in front of us. His buddy was that Jim.

That Jim I hate.

The first place we walked to is called the **Media** Center. My mother calls it a library. It's where the books are. And guess what?

Books are my favorite things in the whole world!

"HEY! THERE'S A **JILLION** OF THEM IN HERE!" I hollered, feeling very excited. "I THINK I LOVE THIS PLACE!"

The **librarian** bent down next to me. She said to use my quiet voice.

"YEAH, ONLY GUESS WHAT? RIGHT NOW I JUST LIKE THE KIND OF BOOKS WITH PICTURES. BUT MOTHER SAYS WHEN I GET BIG, I'M GOING TO LIKE THE KIND WITH JUST WORDS. AND ALSO, **STEW**ED TOMATOES.[3]"

The boy I can beat up said, "Shhh."

I made a **fist** at him.

---

3 **stewed tomatoes** 토마토 스튜. 고기에 버터와 조미료를 넣고, 잘게 썬 토마토와 다른 채소를 섞어 뭉근히 익혀서 만드는 서양식 요리.

Then he turned around.

After that, we went to the **cafeteria**. The cafeteria is where kids eat lunch. Except not when you're in **kindergarten**.

"Ummm!" I said. "It smells **yummy** in here! Just like pasketti[4] and meatballs![5]"

Then that Jim turned around and held his nose.

"P.U.[6] . . . I smell you," he said.

Lucille laughed very hard.

And so I stopped holding her hand.

The next place we went to was the nurse's office.[7]

---

4 **pasketti** 영어권 국가의 어린아이들이 흔히 하는 실수로, 'spaghetti(스파게티)'를 잘못 말한 것이다.

5 **meatball** 미트볼. 곱게 다진 고기에 양파, 빵가루, 달걀 등을 넣고 반죽하여 작게 빚은 후 밀가루와 달걀을 입혀 튀기거나 구워 낸 서양식 요리.

6 **P.U.** '어휴'라는 뜻으로 냄새나 악취가 날 때 혐오감 혹은 역겨움을 나타내는 표현.

It's very cute in that place. There are two little beds where you get to lie down. And two little **blanket**s that are the color of **plaid**.

Our nurse doesn't look like a nurse. She doesn't wear white clothes and white shoes.

Our nurse is just a **regular** color.

Lucille raised her hand. "My brother said that last year he came here. And you let him **take off** his shoes. And he got a drink of water in just his socks!"

That Jim turned around again.

"P.U. . . . I smell your feet," he said to Lucille.

---

7 **nurse's office** 보건실. 학교나 회사에서, 학생이나 사원의 건강이나 위생 등을 위해 적절한 보호 및 관리를 할 수 있는 시설.

This time Lucille stuck out her **tongue** at him.

After that, we held hands again.

5
Principal

After we left the nurse, we went to the main office. That's where the boss of the school lives. His name is Principal.

Principal is a **baldy**.

He talked to us.

Then Lucille raised her hand. "My brother said that last year he had to come down here. And you **yell**ed at him. And now he's not allowed to beat up kids at

recess anymore."

Principal kind of laughed. Then he held the door for us to leave.

After that, we walked to the **water fountain**. And Mrs. let us get a drink. I didn't get a long one, though. 'Cause kids kept **tap**ping on me.

"Hurry up, girl," they said.

"Yeah, only guess what? That's not even my name," I told them.

"Her name is Junie Bumblebee,[1]" said Lucille.

Then she laughed. But I didn't think it was a very funny **joke**.

---

1 **bumblebee** 호박벌. 몸에 검은색과 노란색 털이 난 꿀벌과의 곤충. 여기에서는 루실이 주니 B.의 이름에 있는 B가 'bee(벌)'와 비슷하게 발음되기 때문에 놀리듯 말한 것이다.

After that, Mrs. showed us where the bathrooms were.

There's two kinds of bathrooms in our school. A boys' kind. And a girls' kind. I can't go in the boys' kind, though. 'Cause no girls allowed, that's why.

I tried to **peek** my head in there. But Mrs. **snap**ped her fingers at me.

The only boy who got to go into the bathroom was the boy I can beat up. He was **jiggling** around very much.

Then he started running all over the place. And he was holding the front of his pants.

"William!" said Mrs. "Are you having an **emergency**?"

Then William yelled, "YES!" And he

BOYS

ran right in there.

The rest of us walked back to our room.

I touched Lucille's **fingernail**s. She said that her fingernail **polish** is named Very Very Berry.

"I would like to have my fingernails red, too," I said. "But I'm only allowed to have the kind of polish that makes them look **shiny**. Its name is Clear. Clear is the color of **spit**."

"I hate Clear," said Lucille.

"Me too," I told her. "And also I hate yellow—which is the color of the stupid **smelly** school bus."

Lucille nodded her head. "My brother said when you **ride** home on the bus, kids **pour** chocolate milk on your head."

Then **all of a sudden** my **stomach** felt very squeezy again. 'Cause I had to ride the bus home, that's why.

"Why did you have to tell me that for, Lucille?" I said kind of **grouchy**.

After we got back to Room Nine, we did some more work. It was a game to help us learn each other's names.

I learned Lucille. And also a girl named Charlotte. And another girl named Grace. Then I learned a boy named Ham—which we eat at Grandma Miller's.

Pretty soon Mrs. **clap**ped her loud hands together.

"Okay, everyone. **Gather** up your things. It's almost time for the bell."

Then I heard a noise in the **parking lot**.

It was **screechy brake**s. And so I looked out the window. And I saw the school bus.

It was coming to get me!

"Oh no!" I said kind of loud. "Now I'm going to get chocolate milk poured on my head!" Then I **chew**ed on my fingers.

"Get in line! Get in line!" said Mrs. "When we get outside, I want all of my bus students to come with me. The rest of you must go to the crossing **guard**.[2]"

Everyone was **lining up**. I was the very last one.

Just then the bell rang and Mrs.

---

2 **crossing guard** 교통 안전 요원. 학교 근처에서 활동하는 봉사자로 횡단보도나 교차로 등에서 어린이의 안전한 등하굣길 교통 지도를 담당한다.

marched out the door. Then everybody else marched out, too.

Except guess what?

I didn't.

6
A Good Hider

When you're the very last one in line, nobody watches you. That's how come nobody saw me when I **duck**ed behind the teacher's desk and hid.

I'm a good hider.

One time at Grandma Miller's house, I hid under the kitchen **sink**. Then I made a **growly** sound and **sprung** out at her.

I'm not allowed to do that anymore.

Anyway, I stayed **scrunch**ed behind the teacher's desk for a while. And then I saw a better place to hide. It was the big **supply closet** in the back of the room.

And so I ran back there very fast. And I **squeeze**d onto the bottom **shelf**. I squeezed right on top of the construction

paper.[1]

Most of me was comfortable. **Except** my head was sort of very tight. And my **knee**s were all **bend**ed. Like when I do a **somersault**.

Then I pulled the door mostly closed.

"Don't shut it **all the way**, though. And I *mean* it," I said right out loud.

I stayed real quiet for lots of minutes. Then I heard noises in the **hall**. And some feet came running into the room. Big people's feet, I think.

"What happened?" I heard someone ask.

"One of my little girls is lost," said a

---

1 **construction paper** 색지. 여러 가지 색깔로 물들인 종이로 주로 어린 아이들이 공작 활동을 할 때 사용한다.

voice that sounded like Mrs. "Her name is
Junie B. Jones. And she didn't get on the
bus. So now we've got to go out looking
for her."

Then I heard some keys **jingle**. And the
feet went running out again. And then the
door shut.

I still didn't come out of the closet,
though. When you're a good hider, you
can't come out for a very, very long time.

I just stayed there all bended up. And I
told myself a story. Not an out-loud story.
I just told it inside my head. It was called
"The Little Hiding Girl."

I **made** it **up**. And this is how it went:

Once upon a time there was a little

hiding girl. She was in a secret **spot** where nobody could find her. Except her head was very tight. And her brain was **squish**ing out.

But she still couldn't come out of her spot. Or a smelly yellow **monster** would get her. And also, some **meanie**s with chocolate milk.

The end.

After that, I **rest**ed my eyes.

Resting your eyes is what my grampa does when he watches TV after dinner. Then he **snore**s. And Grandma Miller says, "Go to bed, Frank."

It's not the same thing as a **nap**, though. 'Cause naps are for babies, that's why.

And anyway, I didn't snore. I just did a little **drool**.

Then finally when my eyes were done resting, they woke up.

And so I came out of the closet and ran right to the window. And guess what? There weren't any cars in the parking lot. And no stupid smelly bus, either!

"Whew! That's a **relief**," I said.

A relief is when your **stomach** doesn't feel squeezy anymore.

After that, I went back to the closet. 'Cause while I was hiding, I **sniff**ed the smell of **clay**, that's why. And clay is my very favorite thing in the whole world!

"Hey! I see it up there!" I said.

The clay was on the middle shelf. I stood

on a chair to get it.

It was blue and **stiff**. And so I had to **roll** it on the floor to make it soft and warm. Then I rolled it into a blue orange. It was very beautiful. Except it had some **dirt** and hair on it.

After I was done, I went to the front of the room and sat down in my teacher's big chair. I like teachers' desks very much. The **drawer**s are so big I could **fit** in one, I think.

I opened up the top one. There were happy-face stickers. And **rubber** bands. And also, gold stars—which I love a very lot.

I **stuck** one on my **forehead**.

Then I found paper **clip**s. And red

marking pens.[2] And new pencils with no points. And scissors. And travel **tissue**s. And guess what else?

"**Chalk!**" I said. "**Brand-new** chalk that's not even out of its little box yet!"

Then I stood up on my teacher's chair and **clap**ped my hands together very loud.

"I want everyone to find a chair and sit down! Today we are going to learn some alphabet and some reading. And also, I will teach you how to make a blue orange. But first, everyone has to watch me draw **stuff**."

Then I went to the **board** and drew with my brand-new chalk. I drew a bean and a

---

2 **marking pen** 마킹펜 또는 사인펜. 나일론 등의 합성수지로 된 펜촉을 통해 잉크가 흘러나오도록 만들어진 필기구.

carrot and some **curly** hair.

Then I wrote some O's.

O's are my bestest letter.

After that, I **bow**ed. "Thank you very much," I said. "Now you may all go out for **recess** . . ."

I smiled.

"Except for not that Jim."

7

Peeky Holes and Spying

After a while, I started to get a little bit **thirsty**. That's what happens when **chalk sprinkle**s get in your **throat**.

"I would like a drink of water, I think," I said.

Then I put my hands on my **hip**s. "Yeah, only what if somebody sees you at the **water fountain**? Then they might call the stupid **smelly** bus to come get you.

And so you better not go."

I **stamp**ed my foot. "Yeah, only I *have* to go! 'Cause there's **dumb** chalk in my throat!"

Then **all of a sudden** I got a great idea! I pulled a chair over to the door. And I peeked out the window at the top!

I'm a good peeker.

One time I peeked right into Grampa Miller's mouth when he was sleeping. And I saw that **dangly** thing that hangs down in the back. I didn't touch it, though. 'Cause I didn't have a little stick or anything, that's why.

Anyway, I didn't see anybody in the **hall**. And so I opened the door a **crack**. And I **sniff**ed. 'Cause when you sniff, you can smell if there's people around.

I learned sniffing from my dog, Tickle.
Dogs can smell everything. People can
mostly just smell big smells. Like **stink** and
flowers and dinner.

"Nope. Don't smell anyone," I said.

Then I ran to the water fountain and
I drank for a long time. And nobody
tapped on me and said, "Hurry up, girl."

After that, I stood on my **tip**py-**toe**s.
And I tippy-toed to the **Media** Center.
'Cause I love that place! Remember?

The Media Center is kind of like a **fort**.
The **shelves** are like walls. And the books
are sort of like **brick**s. And you can move
some of them around and make peeky
holes.

Peeky holes are what you spy out of.

Then if you see somebody coming, you can make your breath very quiet. And they won't find you.

I spied for a long time. But nobody came. The only people in the Media Center were just me and some fish.

The fish were in a big glass **tank**. I **wave**d at them in there. Then I **stir**red them with a pencil.

I love fish very much. I eat them for dinner with coleslaw.[1]

Just then I saw my most favorite[2] thing

---

1 **coleslaw** 코울슬로. 잘게 썬 양배추와 여러 가지 채소를 마요네즈 소스에 버무린 음식.

2 **most favorite** '가장 좋아하는'이라는 뜻을 지닌 비격식적인 표현. 원래는 단어 'favorite'이 '선호하는'이라는 의미를 나타내기 때문에 형용사 최상급을 만드는 부사인 'most'를 잘 붙이지 않는다.

in the whole world! Its name is an **electric** pencil **sharpen**er! And it was sitting right on the **librarian**'s desk!

"Hey!" I said very excited. "I think I know how to work that thing!"

Then I looked in the desk **drawer**. And guess what? There were lots of **brand-new** pencils in there!

And so I sharpened them!

It was funner[3] than anything! 'Cause an electric pencil sharpener makes a nice noise. And you can make pencils as **teeny** as you want. You just keep pushing them into the little hole. And they just keep on getting teenier and teenier.

---

3 **funner** 형용사 'fun'의 비교급을 잘못 만든 것으로, 올바른 표현은 'more fun'이다.

It doesn't work on crayons, though. I tried a red one. Then the pencil sharpener slowed way down. And then it made a *rrrrr-rrrrr* sound. And after that, it didn't go anymore.

Just then I heard a noise! It was walking feet. And it made me **scare**d inside. 'Cause I didn't want anyone to find me, that's why!

And so I **squat**ted way down and looked through my peeky hole.

Then I saw a man with a **trash** can! He was singing "Somewhere Over the Rainbow.[4]" That's a song I know. It's from my favorite movie, which is called *The Wizard of Odds*.[5]

The man with the can didn't see me. He walked down the hall. Then I heard him go outside. I stayed squatted down for a long time. But he never came back.

"Whew! That was a close one!" I said.

---

4 **Somewhere Over the Rainbow** 정확한 노래 제목은 'Over the Rainbow'이다. 1939년에 나온 뮤지컬 영화 '오즈의 마법사(The Wizard of Oz)'의 주제가로, 미국의 유명 배우 주디 갈런드(Judy Garland)가 불렀다.

5 **The Wizard of Odds** 영화 'The Wizard of Oz(오즈의 마법사)'의 제목을 잘못 말한 것이다. 이 영화는 캔자스 농장에 살던 소녀 도로시가 회오리에 휩쓸려 신비한 나라 오즈로 가서 겪는 모험을 그렸다.

And so then I ran to find a better place
to hide.

8
The Dangerous Nurse's Office

Guess where I ran to? Straight to the nurse's office, of course! 'Cause there's those little **plaid blanket**s to hide under!

There's other **neat stuff** in there, too. Like a **scale** to **weigh** yourself. And a **sign** with a giant **E** and other letters.

The nurse uses the sign to test your eyes. She points to the letters. And you have to **yell** out their names.

You have to yell the **E** the loudest. That's how come it's so big.

And guess what else I saw in the nurse's office? Band-Aids,[1] that's what! I love those guys!

They were on top of the desk. And so I opened the **lid**. And I sniffed them.

"Ummm," I said. 'Cause Band-Aids smell just like a **brand-new** beach ball.

Then I **dump**ed them out. They were the most prettiest[2] Band-Aids I ever saw! They were red and blue and green! And also yellow. Which is the color I hate.

And they were different shapes, too.

---

1 **Band-Aid** 반창고. 'Band-Aid'는 본래 미국 회사에서 사용하는 상표명이었으나, 반창고를 일컫는 일반적인 용어로 굳어졌다.

2 **most prettiest** 형용사 'pretty'의 최상급을 잘못 만든 것으로, 올바른 표현은 'prettiest'이다.

There were **square**s and circles. And some were that very long kind—which are called tangles,[3] I think.

I put a green circle on my **knee**. That's where I fell down on the **sidewalk** last week. It's mostly all better now. But if I **press** it very hard with my **thumb**, I can still make it hurt.

After that, I put a blue tangle on my finger. That's where I got a **splinter** from the picnic table. Mother pulled it out with **tweezer**s. But there's still some table in there, I think.

Also, I put a red square on my arm. That's where Tickle **scratch**ed me. Because

---

3 **tangle** 여기에서는 주니 B.가 단어 'triangle(삼각형)'이 생각나지 않아 잘못 말한 것이다.

I got him all **wound up**.

Just then I saw the nurse's purple sweater. It was hanging on her chair.

I put it on.

"Now I'm the nurse," I said.

Then I sat down. And I **pretend**ed to call the hospital.

"Hello, hospital? It's me, the nurse. I need some more Band-Aids and some aspirins and some cherry **cough drop**s.[4] Only not the kind that make your mouth feel **freezy**.

"And I need some lollipops[5] for when kids get **needle**s.

---

4 **cough drop** 일시적으로 기침을 멈추게 하고 따가운 목을 달래기 위해 먹는 사탕류의 약.

5 **lollipop** 막대 사탕. 먹기 편하도록 막대 모양의 손잡이를 붙인 사탕.

"And also I need a little **stick** or something **in case** I have to touch that **dangly** thing that hangs down in your **throat**."

Then I pretended to call Room Nine.

"Hello, Mrs.? Please send that Jim to my office. I have to give him a **shot**."

Just then I saw my most favorite thing in the whole world! They were near the door. And their name is **crutch**es!

Crutches are for when you break a leg. Then the doctor puts it in a big white **cast** with just your **piggies** sticking out. And you can't walk on it. And so she gives you crutches to **swing** yourself.

I ran over and picked them up. Then I put them under my arms. Only they were

way too long for me. And I didn't swing
that good.

And so then I got another idea! I
carried them to the nurse's chair. And I
climbed up there so I was real tall. And
then I put the crutches under my arms.
And they **fit**ted just right!

After that, I stood on the **edge** of the
chair. And I **lean**ed forward very slow.

Except then a terrible thing happened!
The chair was on **wheel**s. And it **roll**ed
away from my feet! And I got **stuck** on the
crutches way high in the air! And I was
very dangly up there!

"HEY!" I shouted. "GET ME DOWN
FROM HERE!"

Then I **wiggle**d around. And one of the

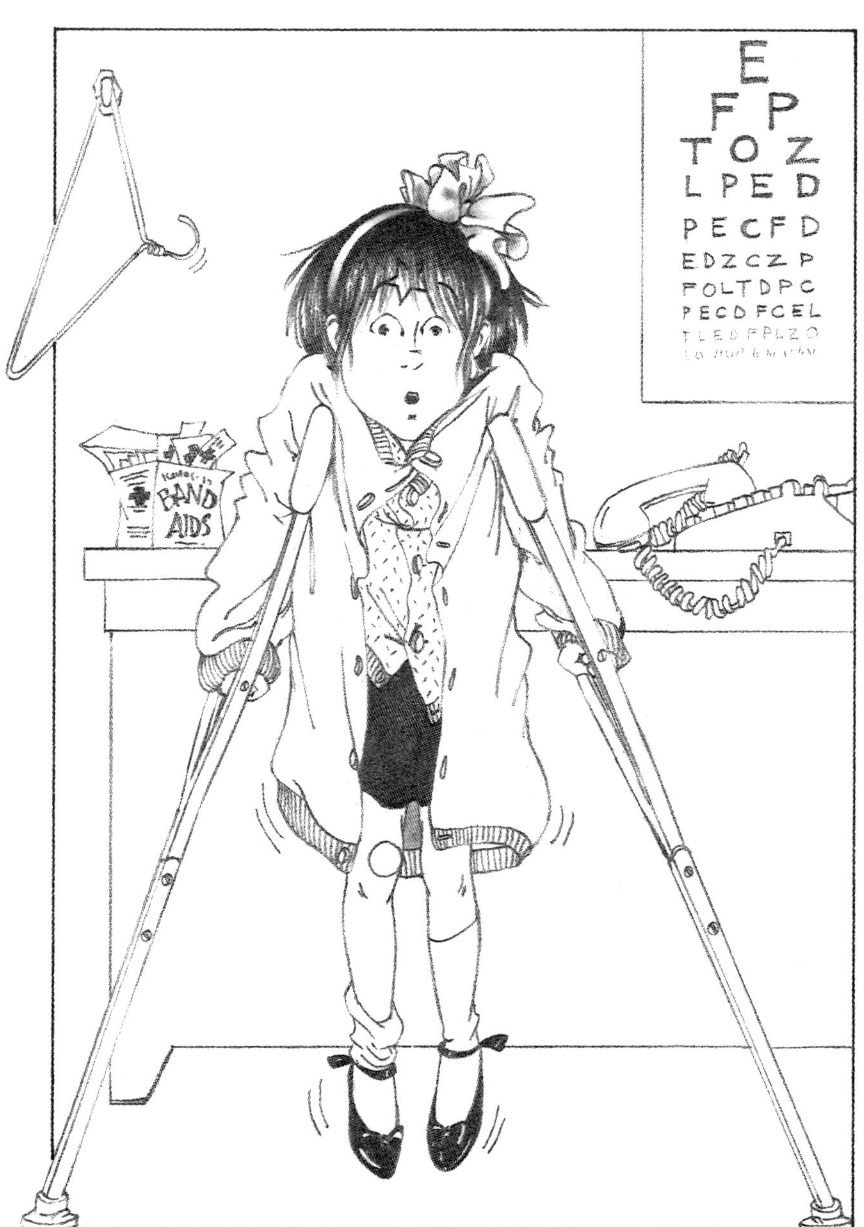
E
F P
T O Z
L P E D
P E C F D
E D Z C Z P
F O L T D P C
P E C D F C E L
BAND AIDS

crutches **slip**ped. And I came **crash**ing down! And I **bang**ed my head on the desk!

"OW!" I yelled. "OW! OW! OW!"

Then I picked up the phone again. "I **quit** this stupid job!" I said.

And then I ran out of there very fast.

'Cause the nurse's office is a dangerous place.

And crutches aren't my favorite thing.

9
Zooming Speedy Fast

I like running inside the school.

It's funner than running inside your house. In school you can zoom with your arms out like a jet plane. And you don't **knock** over the **furniture**. And also the head doesn't get broken off your mother's bird **statue**. Which used to be a blue jay,[1] I think.

I zoomed straight to the **cafeteria**.

'Cause there's a lot of tables to hide under in that place. Only when I tried to open the door, it was all **lock**ed up!

And so then I ran to another room across the **hall**. Only that stupid door was locked, too!

"Hey! Who did all this **dumb** locking?" I asked.

Then I started **jiggling** up and down. 'Cause I was having a little bit of a problem, that's why. The kind of problem that's called *personal*.

And it's about going to the **potty**.

And so **all of a sudden** I had to run

---

1 **blue jay** 파랑어치. 북미 지역에 서식하는 까마귓과의 철새로 대체로 파란색을 띠지만 가슴은 주로 하얗다. 몸의 길이는 약 30센티미터이며 시끄럽게 지저귀는 것이 특징이다.

down the hall speedy quick!

Right to the girls' bathroom!

Only guess what? When I got there, that stupid door wouldn't open, either!

And so I kicked it. And I hanged on the **handle**. 'Cause I **weigh** thirty-seven.

"OPEN UP AND I **MEAN** IT!" I **yell**ed.

But the door kept on staying shut!

"IT'S A '**MERGENCY**!" I shouted.

And then all of a sudden I remembered about that boy I can **beat** up! 'Cause *he* had a 'mergency, too! And *he* got to go into the *boys'* bathroom!

And so I zoomed across the hall. And I pulled on the boys' bathroom door. But that dumb thing was locked, too!

"STUPID, STUPID DOORS!" I **holler**ed.

After that, I started to jiggle up and down very fast. "OH, NO! NOW I'M GONNA HAVE AN **ACCIDENT** ON MY SKIRT THAT LOOKS LIKE VELVET!"

Only just then I remembered something *else* about 'mergencies. 'Cause Mother told me what to do if I ever needed help.

And its name is Call 911![2]

And so then I ran back to the dangerous nurse's office. 'Cause that's where the phone was, of course! And then I picked it up. And I pushed the 9! And the 1! And another 1!

"HELP! THIS IS A 'MERGENCY!" I yelled. "ALL THE DOORS ARE LOCKED

---

2 **911** 우리나라의 긴급 전화번호인 119와 같은 개념으로, 미국과 캐나다에서 범죄나 재난 등 긴급한 일이 발생했을 때 신고하는 전화번호이다.

IN THIS PLACE! AND NOW I'M GOING TO HAVE A TERRIBLE ACCIDENT!"

Then I heard a voice on the other end. She said for me to **calm** down.

"YEAH, ONLY I CAN'T! 'Cause I'M IN BIG TROUBLE! AND I'M ALL **BY MYSELF**! AND I NEED HELP REAL BAD!"

Then the lady said to calm down again. Except for I couldn't stand **still**! And so I just **hung up** and ran right out of there.

And I just kept running and running till I got to the big doors at the end of the hall.

And then I runned right outside! 'Cause maybe there might be a little **toilet** out there or something.

Except I didn't see one. All I could hear was **siren**s! Loud sirens were all over the place.

And they kept on getting closer and closer! And then a big green **fire truck** came zooming right around the corner! And a white police car! And a fast red **ambulance**!

And guess what else? They turned right into the school **parking lot**!

And so I stopped jiggling for a second. And I **sniff**ed the air. Only I couldn't smell any **smoke**!

Then I heard a **grouchy** voice. "HEY! **HOLD IT**, MISSY!" it yelled.

And I got very **scare**d inside. 'Cause missy's my name when I'm in trouble.

I turned around. It was the man with the can! And he was running at me!

"HOLD IT RIGHT THERE!" he hollered again.

And then I started to cry.

"Yeah, only that's the trouble. I can't hold it!" I said. "I already holded it all I can! And now I'm having a 'mergency!

And all the bathrooms are locked! And now I'm going to have an accident very quick!"

And then the man with the can didn't look so grouchy anymore.

"Well, why didn't you say so, sis!3" he

---

3 **sis** '아가씨' 또는 '언니'라는 뜻으로 여자아이나 젊은 여자를 부를 때 사용하는 비격식적인 호칭이다.

said.

Then he pulled a big **bunch** of keys out of his pocket. And he **grab**bed my hand.

And then him and me zoomed back into the school! Speedy fast!

10
Me and That Grace

The man with the can un**lock**ed the girls'
bathroom for me. And I ran right in there.

And guess what? I **made it**! That's what!
I didn't have an **accident** on my skirt that
looks like velvet!

"Whew! That was a close one!" I said.

Then I washed my hands at the **sink**.
And I looked in the mirror. And the gold
star was still on my **forehead**!

It looked very beautiful up there!

After that, I went into the **hall** and the man with the can **bend**ed down to me.

"Everything okay, sis?" he said.

And so I **nod**ded my head. "I holded it," I said very happy.

Then **all of a sudden** there were lots of people running at us.

There were firemen. And policemen. And there was a tall lady **roll**ing a bed on **wheel**s.

"Hey!" I said to the man with the can. "What happened? Did somebody get **run**ned **over** in here or something?"

Then I saw Mrs. and **Principal** and Mother. They were running at us, too.

And then Mother bended down and

hugged me very tight!

After that everyone started talking **at once**. And nobody was using their quiet voices. And nobody was smiling, either.

Principal started asking me a **jillion** questions. Mostly they were questions about hiding in the **supply closet**.

"I'm a good hider," I told him.

Principal acted a little bit **grumpy**. He said I wasn't allowed to do that anymore.

"When you go to school, you have to follow the **rule**s," he said. "What would happen if every boy and girl hid in the supply closet after school?"

"It would be very **smush**y in there," I said.

Then he made his eyes **frown**y. "But we

wouldn't know where anyone was, would we?" he said.

"Yes," I said. "We would all be in the supply closet."

Then Principal looked up at the **ceiling**. And I looked up, too. But I didn't see anything again.

After that, Mother looked at my Band-Aids. "Did you hurt yourself?" she asked.

And so I told her all about the dangerous nurse's office. And then I showed her the nurse's purple sweater. And she made me give it back.

After that, everybody started leaving. The firemen. And the policemen. And also the tall lady with the bed.

Then finally, my mother got to take me

home. And guess what? I didn't have to **ride** on the stupid **smelly** bus.

Except the car wasn't that fun. 'Cause Mother was **grouchy** at me.

"I'm sorry the bus wasn't fun for you, Junie B.," she said. "But what you did was very, very wrong. Didn't you see all the **commotion** you caused? You had a *lot* of people very **scare**d."

"Yes, but I didn't want chocolate milk **pour**ed on my head," I explained to her.

"That's *not* going to happen," **growl**ed Mother. "And you can't just suddenly decide for yourself not to ride the bus. *Hundreds* of kids ride buses every day. And if they can do it, you can do it, too."

Then my eyes got wet again. "Yeah, but

there's **meanie**s on that thing," I said all
sniffly.

Then Mother stopped being so **growly**.

"What if you had a friend to ride with?"
she said. "Your teacher told me there's a
girl in your class who will be riding the
bus for the first time tomorrow. Maybe you
could sit together. Would you like that?"

I made my shoulders go up and down.

"Her name is Grace," said Mother.

"Grace?" I said. "Hey! I know that Grace!
I learned her today!"

And so when we got home, Mother
called that Grace's mother. And then
they talked. And then me and that Grace
talked, too. I said hi and she said hi. And
she said she would sit with me.

And so tomorrow I get to take my little red **purse** on the bus. And I get to put it on the seat next to me so nobody will sit there.

Nobody except for that Grace, of course.

And then she and me might get to be **buddies**. And we can hold hands. Just like me and Lucille.

I will like that, I think.

And guess what else?

Tomorrow I think I might like yellow a little bit, too.